This book belongs to:

Name

Address   19   Egerton park
          Worsley
          manchester   M28 2TR

"I am going to marry Celeste.
We will give a grand party
to celebrate our marriage
and our coronation".

JEAN DE BRUNHOFF
BABAR'S
Birthday
Book

METHUEN CHILDREN'S BOOKS

First published in 1992
by Methuen Children's Books
A division of Reed International Books Limited
Michelin House, 81 Fulham Road, London SW3 6RB

Text and illustrations by Jean de Brunhoff
from *The Story of Babar, Babar's Travels,*
Babar the King, Babar at Home, Babar's Friend Zephir
and *Babar and Father Christmas.*

Printed and bound in Hong Kong

ISBN 0 416 18714 5

JEAN DE BRUNHOFF
BABAR'S
Birthday
Book

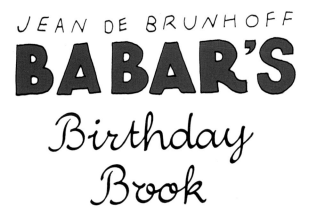

He was amazed, for it was the
first time he had seen so
many houses.

JANUARY

1	2
3	4

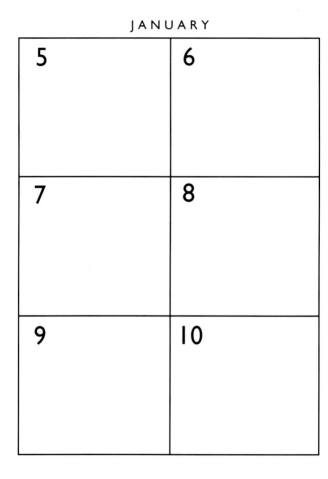

5

6

7

8

9

10

11

12

13

14

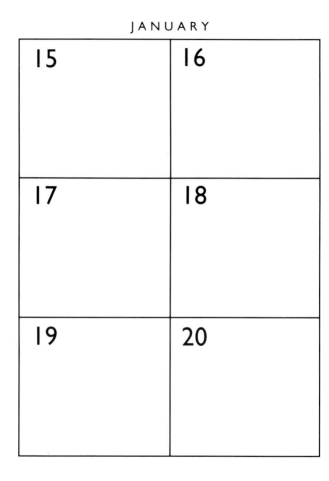

15

16

17

18

19

20

21

22

23

24

25

26

Babar was so pleased with his purchases, and satisfied with his appearance that he paid a visit to the photographer.

In the evenings, after dinner,
he told the old lady's friends
all about his life in the
Great Forest.

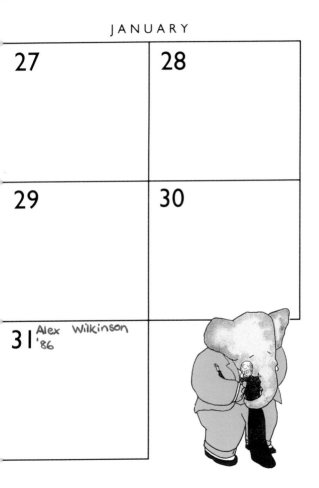

Every day he drove out in the ca
that the old lady had bought him

FEBRUARY

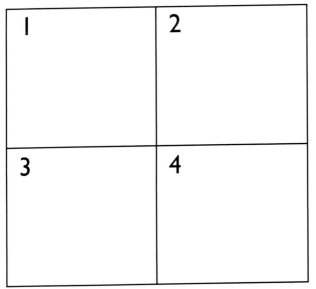

1	2
3	4

Two years passed by. One day he was out for a walk, when he met two little elephants with no clothes on. "Why, here are Arthur and Celeste, my two little cousins!" he cried in amazement to the old lady.

Babar hugged Arthur and Celeste
and took them to buy some lovely clothes.

5	6

Next, he took them to a tea-shop,

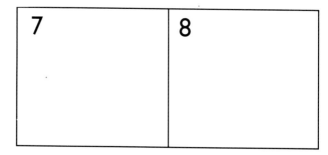

7	8

where they had some delicious cakes.

9	10

FEBRUARY

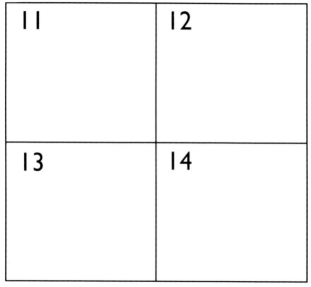

| 11 | 12 |
| 13 | 14 |

15	16
17	18
19	20

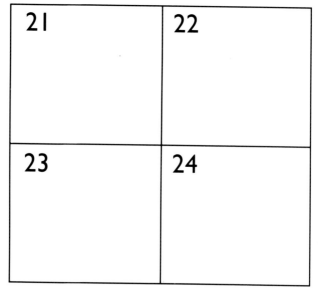

21

22

23

24

25	26
27	28
29	

Babar arrived after a
difficult journey at the little
town ~~of~~ PRJMNESTWE.

MARCH

1	2
3 John '95	4

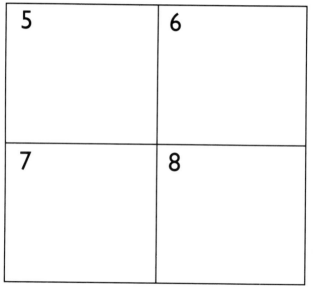

5

6

7

8

They needed a
few days' rest before
returning to the land of the elephants,
so went to the mountains for a
change of air and some ski-ing.

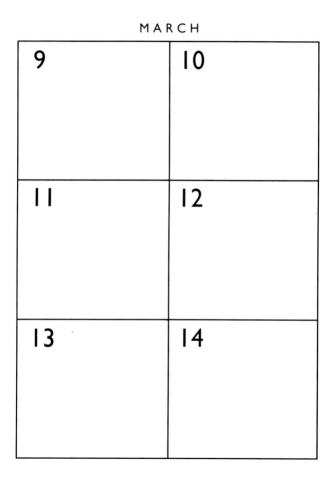

15

16 Mum '65
Birthday

17

18

19

20

21

22

23

24

| 25 | 26 |

"We must build our town here. Our houses will be by the water in the midst of flowers and birds."

APRIL

1 Tamasis Ellis Birthday	2
3	4

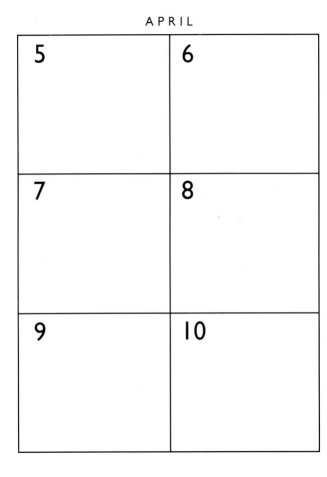

5	6
7	8
9	10

| 11 | 12 |

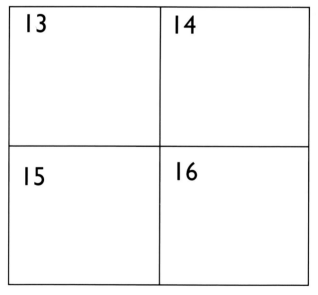

13

14

15

16

17	18
19 *Leonard Birthday*	20

21

22

23

24

25

26

The gardeners had plenty to do,
raking the paths, watering the flowers,
and planting out the beds.

Babar, with Arthur and Zephir, is sailing round in his boat, admiring his new Capital.

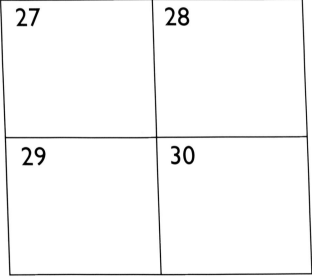

27

28

29

30

Babar, and his wife, Queen Celeste,
went away for their honeymoon
in a yellow balloon.

M A Y

1	2 David Beckham 1.75
3	4

5 Eleri Sullivan '83?

6

7

8

MAY

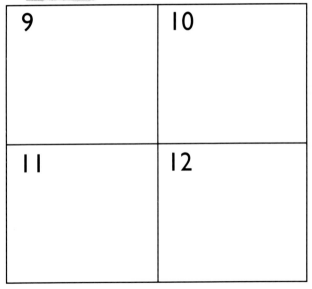

9	10
11	12

13

14 Lauren. Garton '86

15

16

17

18

"Good morning, Lady Whale,
I am Babar, King of the elephants,
and this is my wife, Celeste."

19	20

21	22
23	24

25

26

27	28
29	30
31	

TAPITOR CAPOULOSSE FANDAGO BARBACOL

PODULAR PILOPHAGE JUSTINIEN DOULAMOR

POUTIFOUR HATCHIBOMBOTAR OLUR COCO

The elephants who
were too old to go to school
each chose a profession or trade

JUNE

1	2
3	4

5

6

7

8

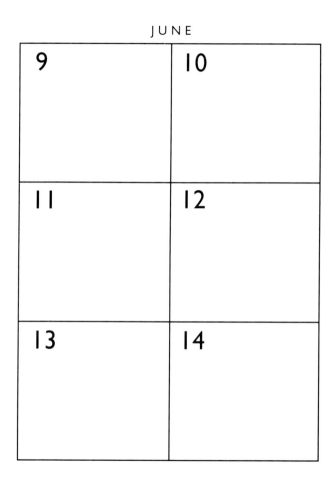

9	10
11	12
13	14

15

16

Babar arranged that
on the following Sunday the
elephants should have
a Garden Party.

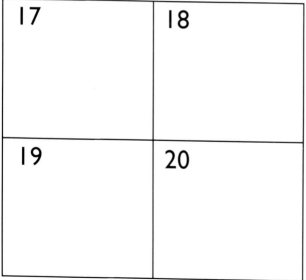

17	18
19	20

21	22
23	24
25	26

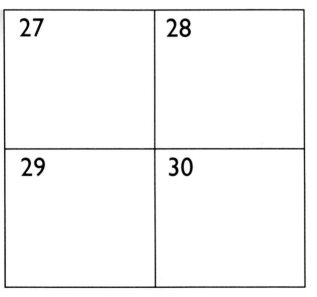

27

28

29

30

Behold Celesteville!
The elephants have just
finished building it, and are
now resting or bathing.

JULY

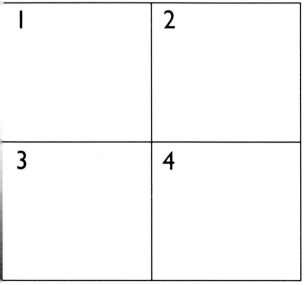

1

2

3

4

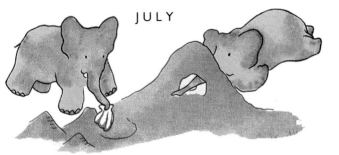

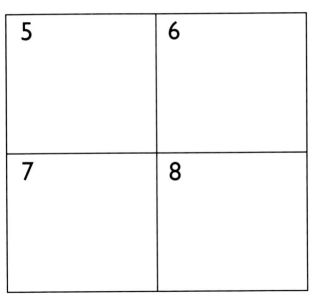

| 5 | 6 |
| 7 | 8 |

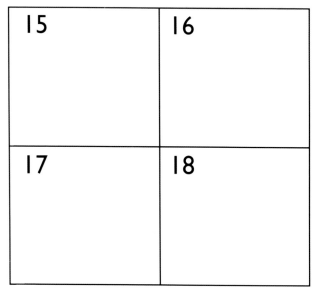

15	16
17	18

19	20
21	22

23

24

| 25 | 26 |

27	28
29	30
31	

What a wonderful sight they sa
It was Babar arriving in his ca

AUGUST

1	2
3	4

5	6
7 Hannahs Birthday	8

9

10

King Babar and Queen Celeste led a
happy life in the country of the
elephants. Their friend, the old lady,
had gladly agreed to stay with them.

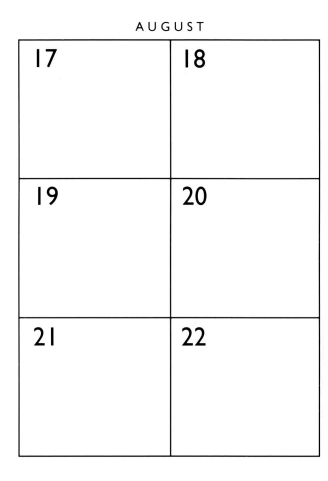

17

18

19

20

21

22

23	24

25	26

27

28

29

30

31

A learned professor gave him
lessons. Babar was attentive, and
always gave the right answer.
He was a most promising pupil.

SEPTEMBER

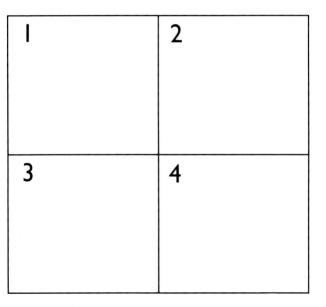

1

2

3

4

5	6
7	8
9	10

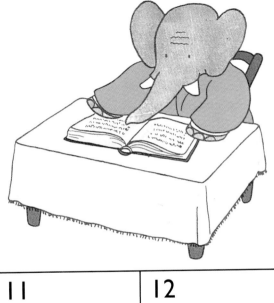

11	12

13

14

15

16

17	18
19	20

| 21 | 22 |
| | |

23	24

25	26

27	28
29	30

"My dear friends,
we must have a new King.
Why not choose Babar?"

OCTOBER

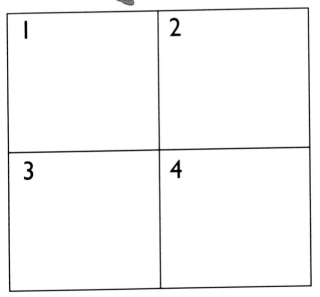

1	2
3	4

5	6
7	8
9	10

11

12

13

14

15

16

"Long live Queen Celeste!
Long live King Babar!"

17

18

19

20

OCTOBER

21	22
23 Katherine '85	24
25	26

27	28
29 Dad 'BA Birthday	30
31	

Celeste had only got one cradle,
so the nurse quickly made another
out of a basket, a napkin
and an umbrella.

NOVEMBER

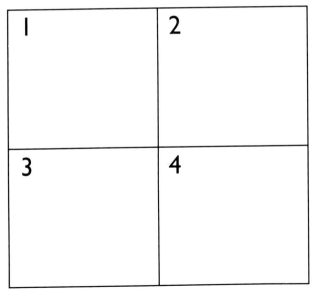

1	2
3	4

NOVEMBER

| 5 | 6 |
| 7 | 8 Fazila Ravat '85 |

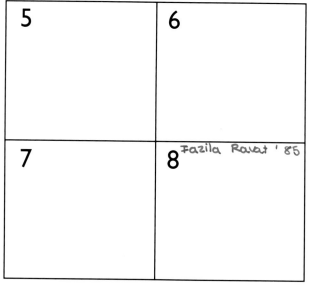

9

10

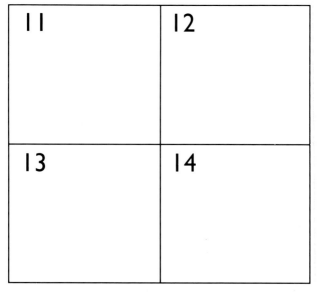

11	12
13	14

15	16
17	18
19	20

21	22 Louise Tom Kou Birthday

23	24
25	26
27	28

29	30

They arrived. Father Christmas
admired the scenery. Elephants
came running from all directions
to welcome him.

DECEMBER

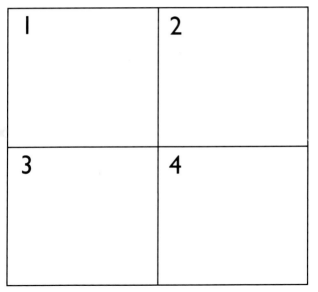

1	2
3	4

5

6

DECEMBER

7	8
9	10

11

12

13

14

"You shall take my place on Christm

15	16

"Eve in the land of the elephants".

17	18

DECEMBER

19	20
21 Anisha Sukha '85	22
23	24 Laura Dodson '85

25	26

DECEMBER

27	28
29	30
31	